PIANO LOUNGE

Favourites

Wise Publications
part of The Music Sales Group
London/New York/Paris/Sydney/Copenhagen/Berlin/Madrid/Tokyo

Published by
Wise Publications
14-15 Berners Street, London W1T 3LJ, UK.

Exclusive Distributors:
Music Sales Limited
Distribution Centre, Newmarket Road, Bury St Edmunds,
Suffolk IP33 3YB, UK.
Music Sales Pty Limited
120 Rothschild Avenue, Rosebery, NSW 2018, Australia.

Order No. AM990869
ISBN: 978-1-84772-139-6
This book © Copyright 2007 Wise Publications,
a division of Music Sales Limited.

Edited by Rachel Payne.
Printed in the EU.

Your Guarantee of Quality:
As publishers, we strive to produce every book to the highest
commercial standards. This book has been carefully designed to minimise
awkward page turns and to make playing from it a real pleasure.
Particular care has been given to specifying acid-free, neutral-sized
paper made from pulps which have not been elemental chlorine bleached.
This pulp is from farmed sustainable forests and was produced with
special regard for the environment.
Throughout, the printing and binding have been planned to ensure a sturdy,
attractive publication which should give years of enjoyment.
If your copy fails to meet our high standards, please inform us and
we will gladly replace it.

www.musicsales.com

Ain't Misbehavin'

Music by Thomas 'Fats' Waller & Harry Brooks

TO CODA

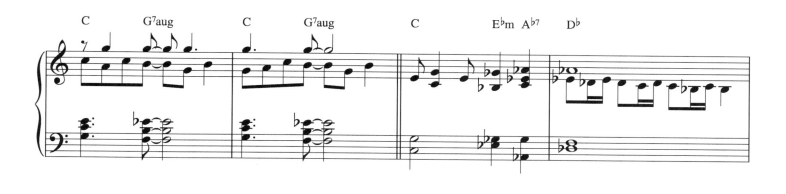

D.S. al CODA

CODA

Beyond The Sea

Music by Charles Trenet

Both Sides Now

Music by Joni Mitchell

Come Fly With Me

Music by James Van Heusen

Desafinado
(Slightly Out Of Tune)

Music by Antonio Carlos Jobim

19

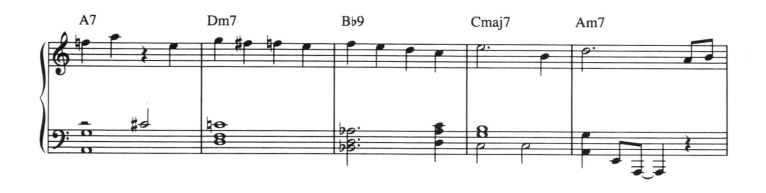

Don't Know Why

Music by Jesse Harris

The Girl From Ipanema
(Garota De Ipanema)

Music by Antonio Carlos Jobim

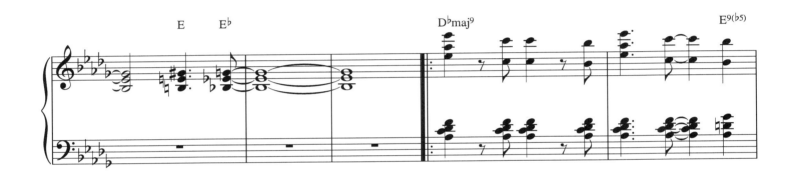

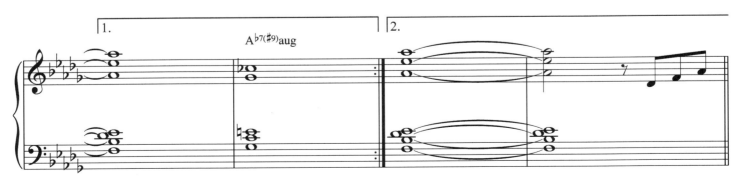

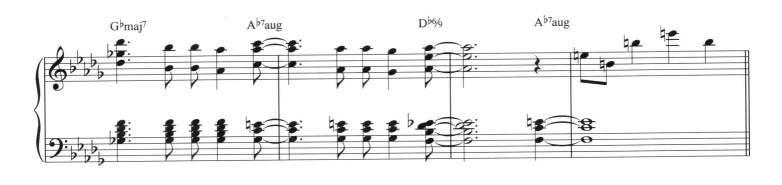

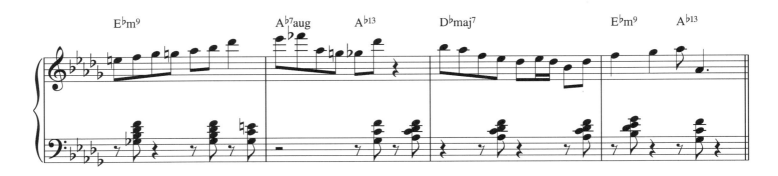

28

Have I Told You Lately

Music by Van Morrison

Here, There And Everywhere

Music by John Lennon & Paul McCartney

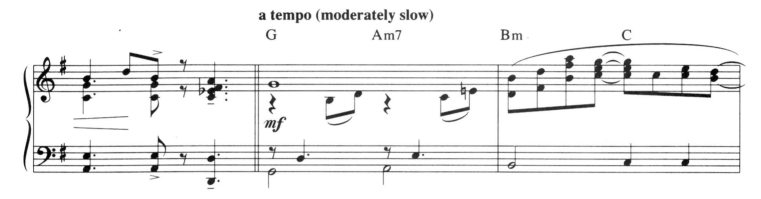

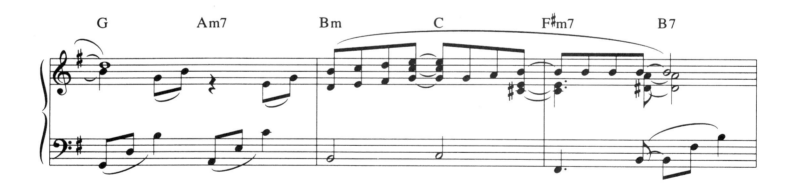

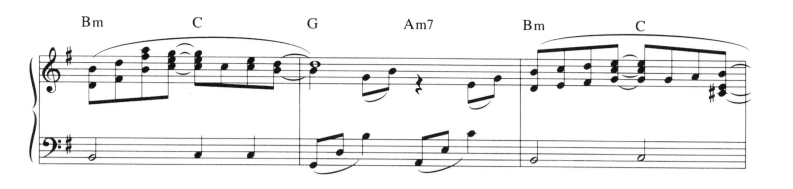

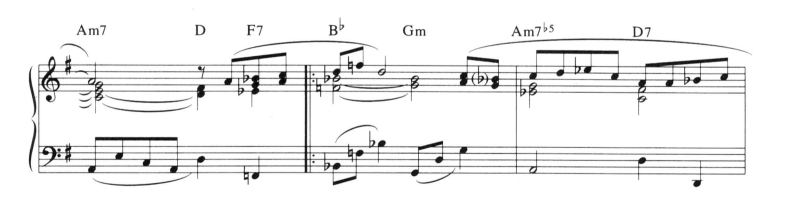

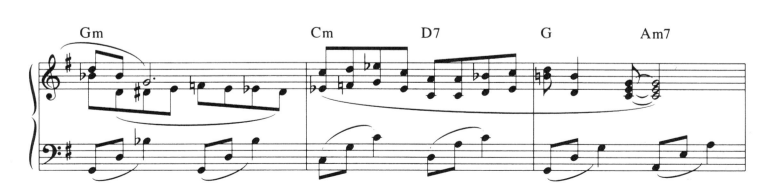

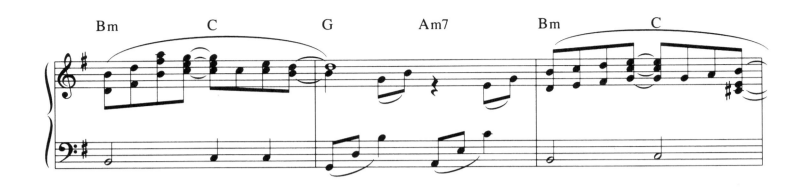

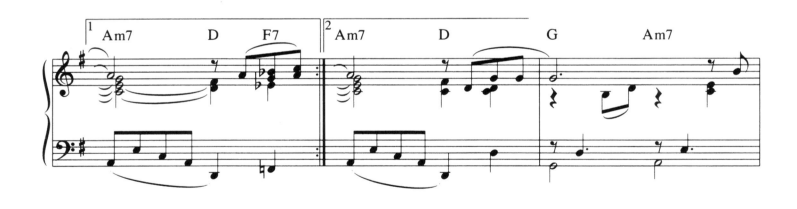

How Insensitive

Music by Antonio Carlos Jobim

In A Sentimental Mood

Music by Duke Ellington, Irving Mills & Manny Kurtz

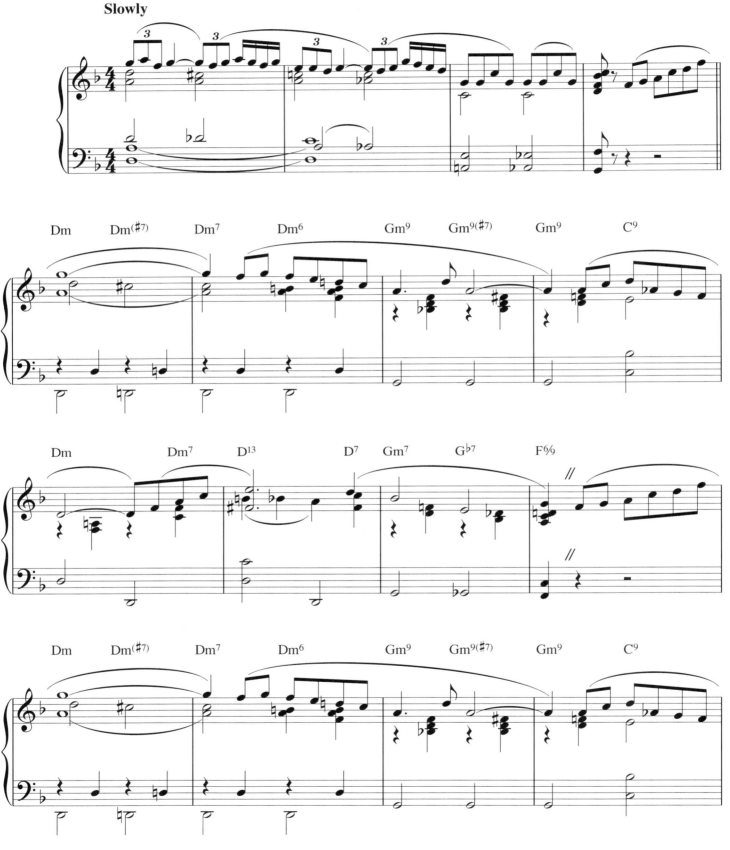

Lullaby Of Birdland

Music by George Shearing

Moon River

Music by Henry Mancini

Moderately

Misty

Music by Erroll Garner & Johnny Burke

50

Smoke Gets In Your Eyes

Music by Jerome Kern

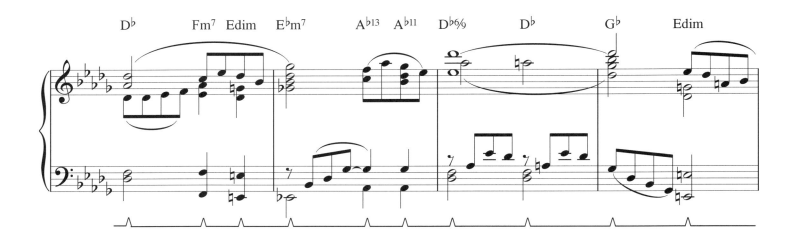

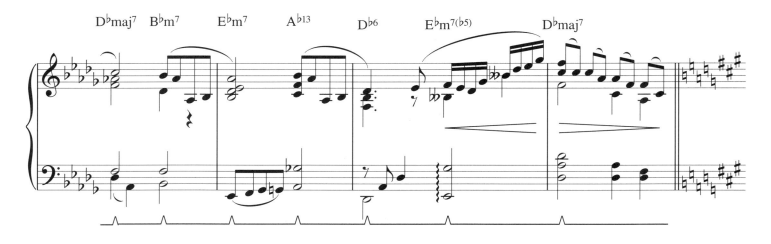

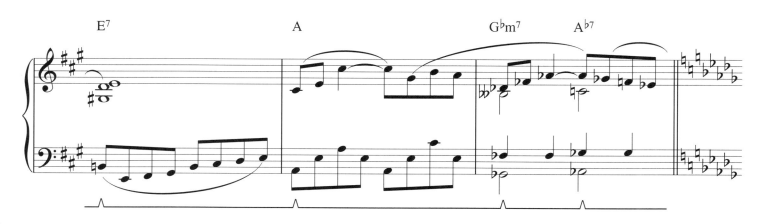

She

Music by Charles Aznavour

That's Amore

Music by Harry Warren & Jack Brooks

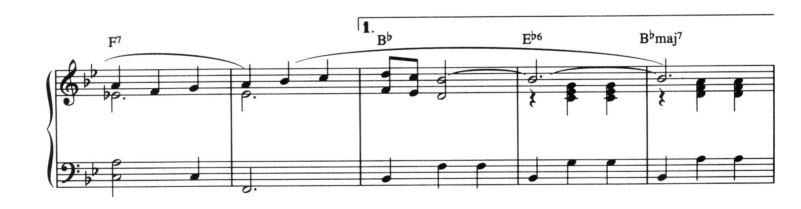

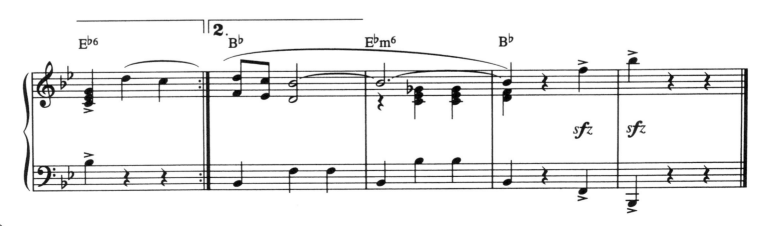

What A Wonderful World

Music by George Weiss & Bob Thiele

The Very Thought Of You

Music by Ray Noble

Walk On By

Music by Burt Bacharach

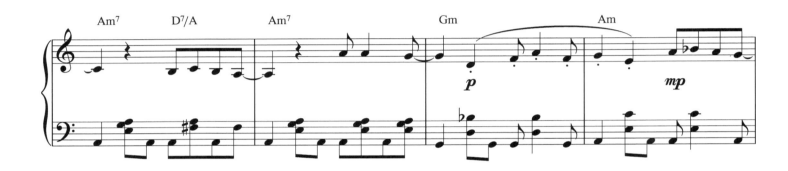

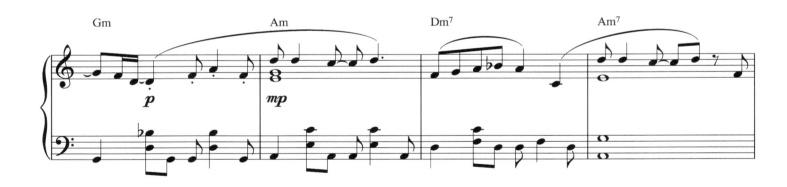

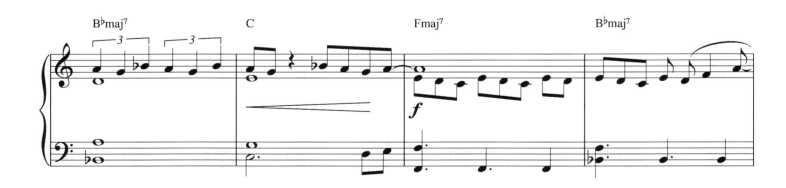

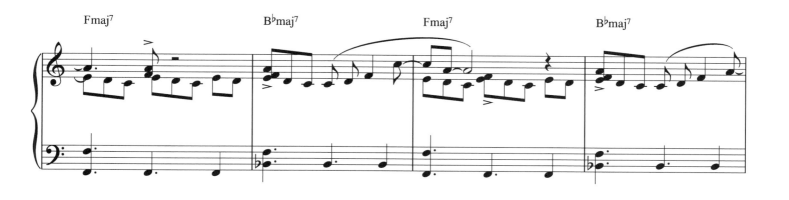

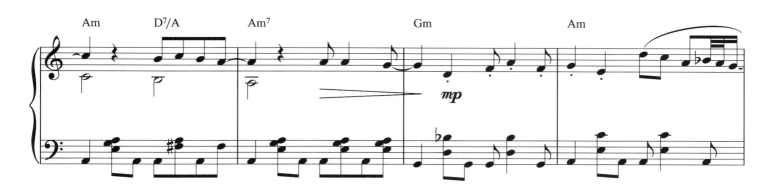

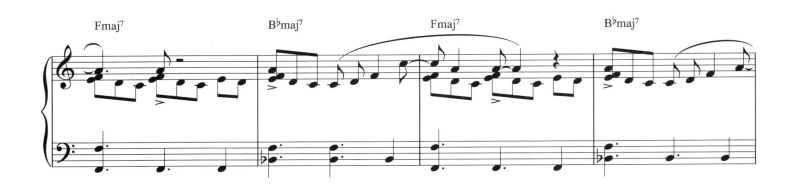

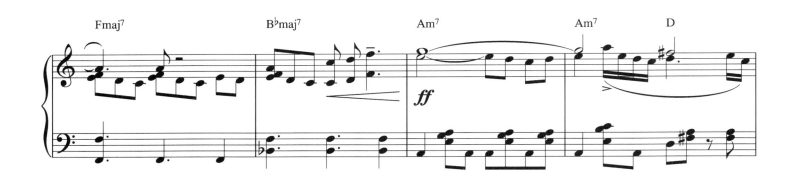

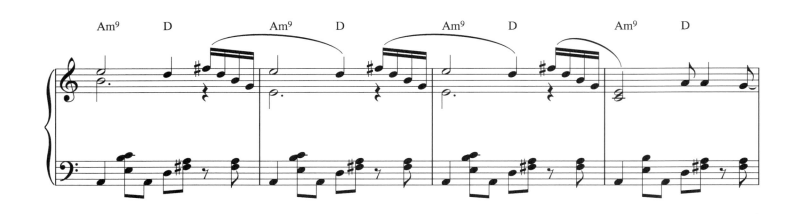

70

What The World Needs Now Is Love

Music by Burt Bacharach

Where Do I Begin
(Theme from 'Love Story')

Music by Francis Lai

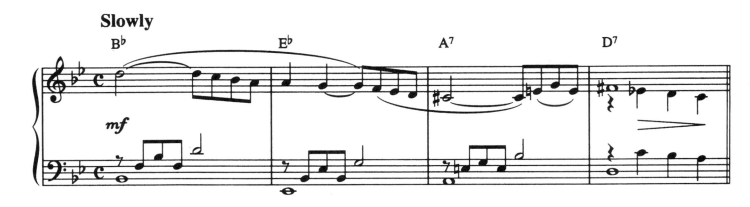

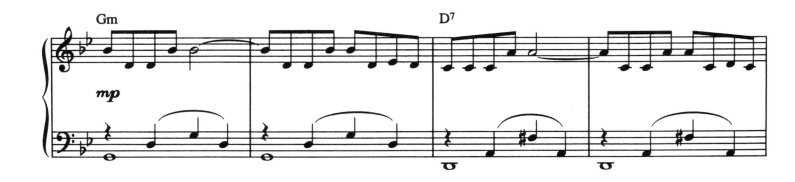

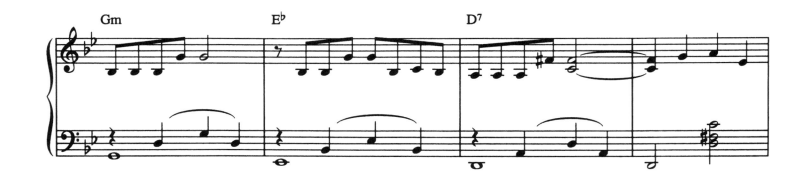

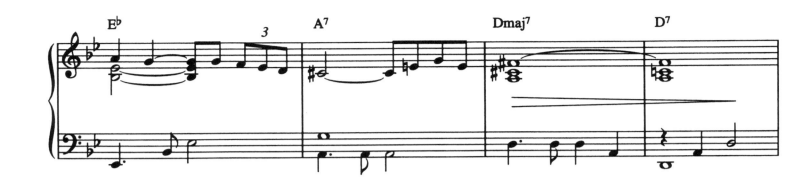

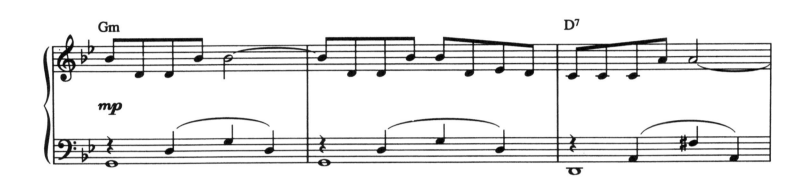

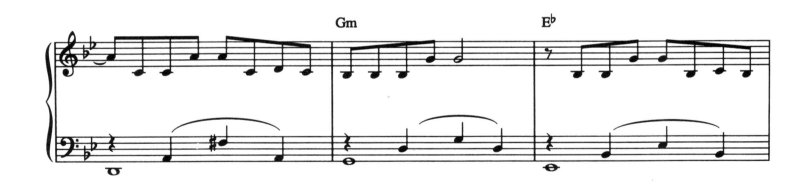

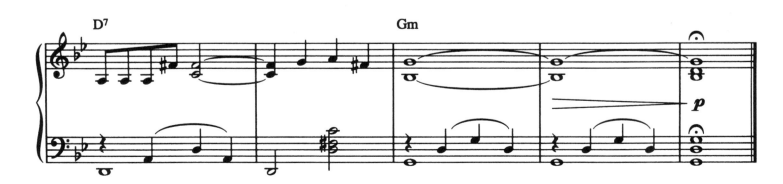

Yesterday Once More

Music by Richard Carpenter & John Bettis

If you like this book you will also like these...

CLASSIC ADS
22 classic themes and music made popular by T.V. adverts.
Includes: Adagio for Strings (The Times), 633 Squadron (Zurich), Johnny and Mary (Renault Clio), Fields of Gold (Cancer Research).
Order No. CH65989

THE PIANIST
Music by Chopin from the ACADEMY AWARD and BAFTA nominated film. *The Pianist.*
Arranged for piano solo.
Order No. CH66583

CLASSICAL CHILLOUT
Sit down at the piano and chill out with some of the world's most soothing melodies.
Includes: Clair de Lune (Debussy), Gymnopédie No.1 (Satie), Sarabande in D minor (Handel) and The Heart Asks Pleasure First from *The Piano* (Nyman).
Order No. CH64053

CLASSICAL CHILLOUT GOLD
Unwind with this great sequel to our best selling *classical chillout* containing 29 super cool piano favourites to play and enjoy.
Includes: Adagio for Strings (Barber), The Lamb (Tavener), Pavane (Fauré)
Order No. CH66319

THE GOLD SERIES
A beautifully presented series of albums containing the most famous masterpieces from the world's greatest composers.

MOZART GOLD
Includes: A Musical Joke, Piano Concerto No.21 'Elvira Madigan', Serenade in B♭ 'Gran Partita' and Symphony No.40 in G minor.
Order No. CH65505

BEETHOVEN GOLD
Includes: Symphony No.5, Für Elise, Minuet in G and the 'Moonlight' Sonata.
Order No. CH65670

CHOPIN GOLD
Includes: All famous waltzes, nocturnes, preludes and mazurkas as well as excerpts from Piano Concerto No.1, Ballade in G minor and Sonata No.2 in B♭ Minor.
Order No. CH65681

TCHAIKOVSKY GOLD
Includes: 1812 Overture, plus music from The Nutcracker, Sleeping Beauty and Swan Lake.
Order No. CH65692